What Is A Simple Machine

By Gene Darby

Pictures — Robert W. Friedl

BENEFIC PRESS · CHICAGO

Publishing Division of Beckley-Cardy Company

Atlanta   **Dallas**   **Long Beach**   **Portland**

The WHAT IS IT Series

What Is A Bird
What Is A Cow
What Is A Fish
What Is A Frog
What Is A Plant
What Is A Tree

What Is Air
What Is Light
What Is Heat
What Is A Cell
What Is Water
What Is Sound
What Is Space
What Is A Star
What Is A Bee
What Is Soil
What Is Gravity
What Is A Rock
What Is Energy
What Is A Reptile

What Is A Season
What Is A Turtle
What Is A Chicken
What Is The Earth
What Is A Butterfly
What Is A Simple Machine

What Is Matter
What Is A Magnet
What Is A Rocket
What Is A Rodent
What Is A Solar System
What Is A Human
What Is A Machine
What Is Chemistry
What Is Weather
What Is Electricity
What Is An Atom
What Is An Insect
What Is A Dinosaur
What Is Electronic Communication

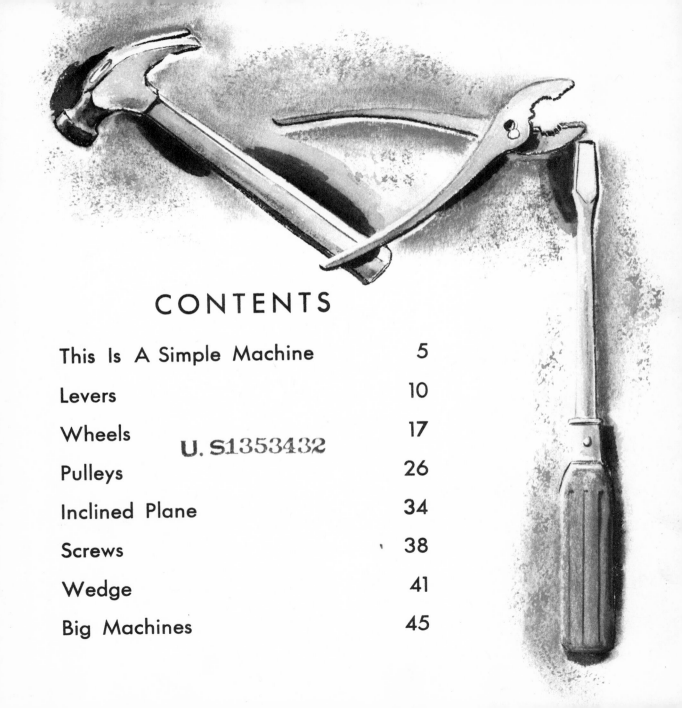

CONTENTS

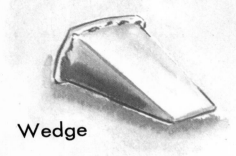

Wedge

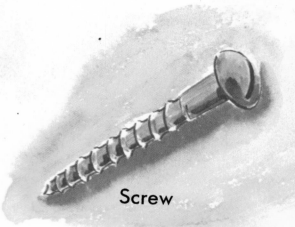

Screw

Wheel

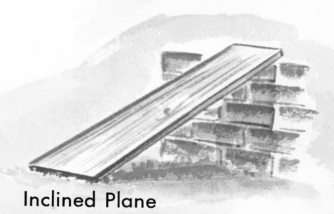

Inclined Plane

Pulley

Lever

THIS IS A SIMPLE MACHINE

Here are the six simple machines.

People use the simple machines to do work.

People use the simple machines to make big machines.

This can be a simple machine.

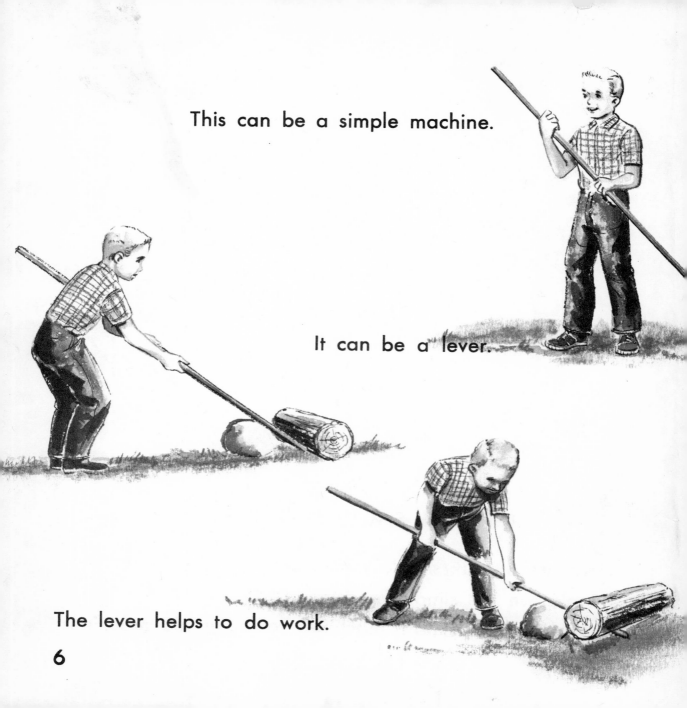

It can be a lever.

The lever helps to do work.

6

This is a simple machine, too.
It is a wheel.

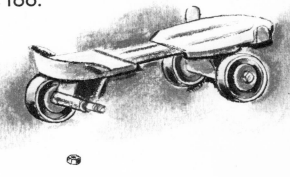

It helps to make things go.

A pulley is a simple machine.
It helps to move things up, down, or across.

This simple machine is an inclined plane.
People walk on it.
Animals walk on it.

They can go

and

up,   down,

up,   down,

up,   down.

LEVERS

All of these
are levers.

See the work
they do.

10

The boy and the girl
are on a lever.
    They can go up
and down.

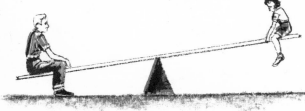

The man gets on the lever.
The girl cannot go down.
The man is too big.
The girl is too little.

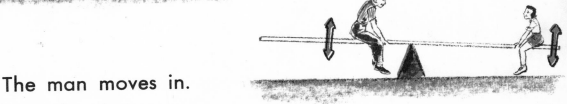

    The man moves in.
See what happens.

The man will use a lever to help move the big rock.

He cannot move the rock.

See what the man is doing.
He moves the log.

Now the man can move the rock.

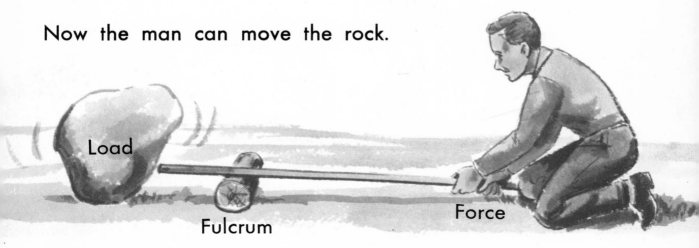

Load

Fulcrum

Force

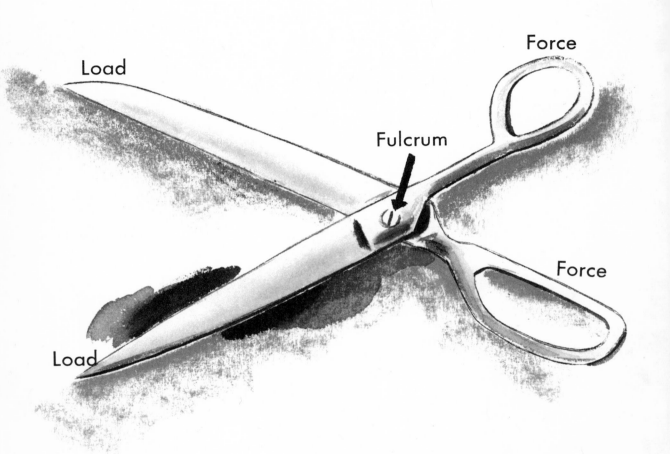

This machine has two levers.

This is a kind of lever, too.
See what is in the middle.

Force

Force

Load

Fulcrum
(Axle)

15

This is a lever, too.
See how it works.

WHEELS

Pull,

pull,

pull.

The boy is putting
something under
his wagon.

Now the wagon will go!

It will not go very far.
See what happens.

18

Saw, saw, saw.
The boy makes wheels.

The wheels go on the wagon.

Now the wagon will go and go!

Some wheels have teeth.

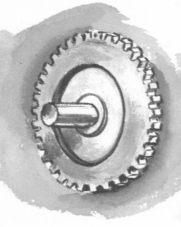

Wheels with teeth
are called gears.

The teeth of gears
can go this way.
One gear can turn the other gear.

See the gears turn.

Cars have gears.

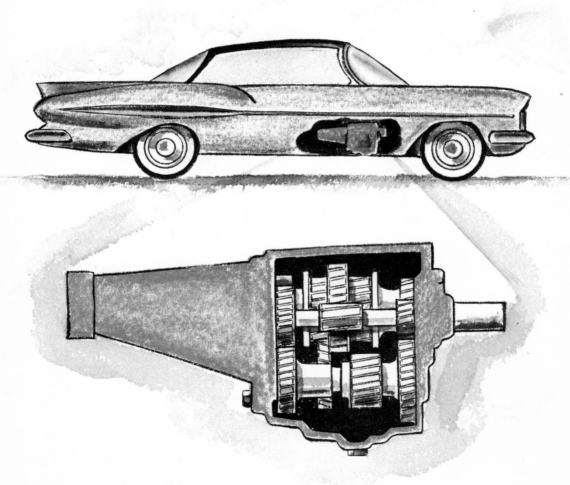

Bicycles have gears.

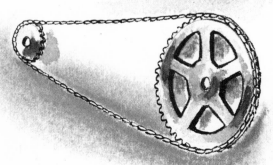

The teeth of bicycle gears
are not together.
See what makes the gears turn.

All of these little things have wheels.

All of these big things have wheels.

PULLEYS

This simple machine
is a pulley.

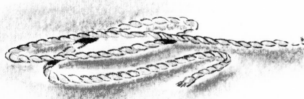

It is made
of a rope.

It is made
of a wheel.

26

Around and around
goes the pulley wheel.

Up comes the flag.

Down goes
the rope.

27

Pulleys can help many things go up and down.

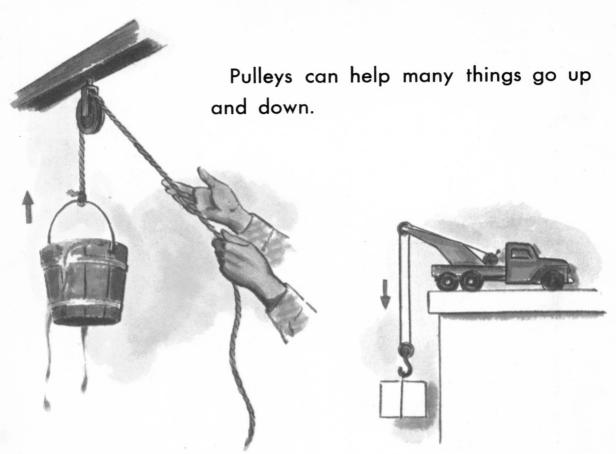

Pulleys help move things across.

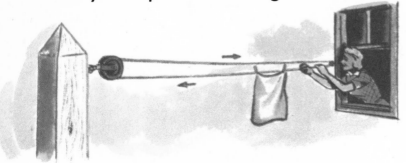

This kind of pulley moves.

The pulley helps move
the big box across.
See the wheel move
along the rope.

The pulley helps
the boy.
Pull, pull, pull.
Up goes the wheel.
Up goes the box!

Pulleys help take things off the boat.
Look at the elephant.
See it ride.
It rides with the help of the pulley.

This is a block and tackle.
It is made of two pulleys.

This pulley does not move.

This pulley moves.

See the rope.
See where it goes.
Find the numbers. 1 2

This is a block and tackle, too.
It can do more work.
You know this by the way the rope goes.
Find the numbers on the rope.
1 2 3 4

INCLINED PLANE

The board is down.

The board is up.

When the boy puts the board this way, he has an inclined plane.

Up he goes on the inclined plane.

Find the door of the airplane.
Find the people.
The people cannot get into the airplane.

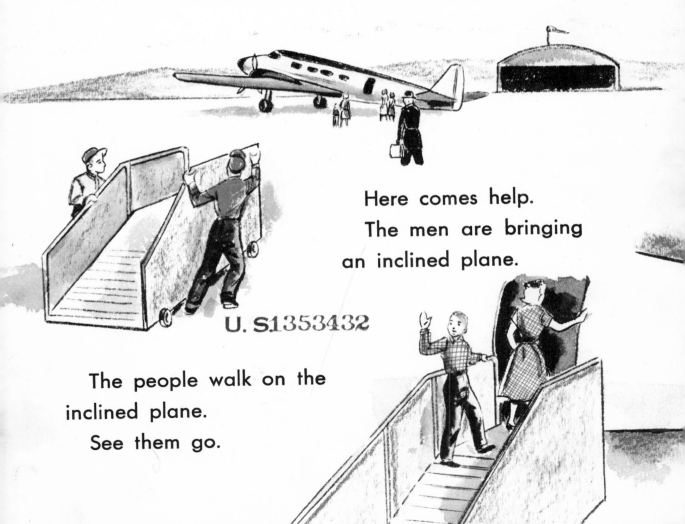

Here comes help.
The men are bringing
an inclined plane.

U. S1353432

The people walk on the
inclined plane.
See them go.

Trains go on inclined planes.

Cars go on inclined planes.

An inclined plane helps
in other ways.
Roll, roll, roll.
Up it goes.
It goes up the inclined plane.

37

SCREWS

A screw is an inclined
plane, too.

It is an inclined plane
that goes around and around.

Up and up, around and
around goes the inclined
plane.

Down and around
goes the screw.
The screw can hold.

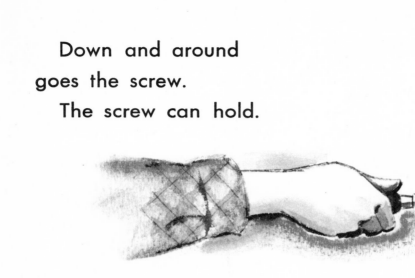

Screws can hold up
big things.

Down come the children.
Down they come on an inclined plane.

This inclined plane is big.
It helps children to play.

WEDGE

A wedge is made of two inclined planes.

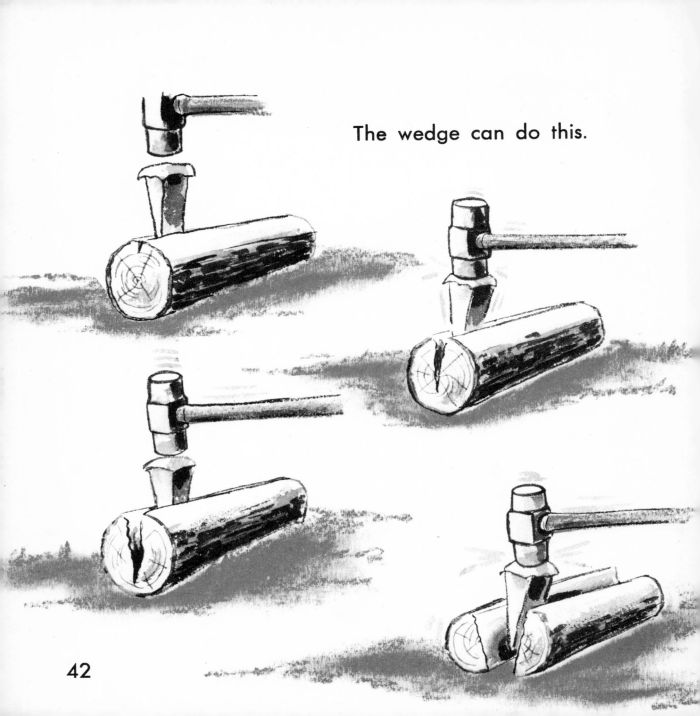

The wedge can do this.

See the wedge.

The man works
with a wedge.

43

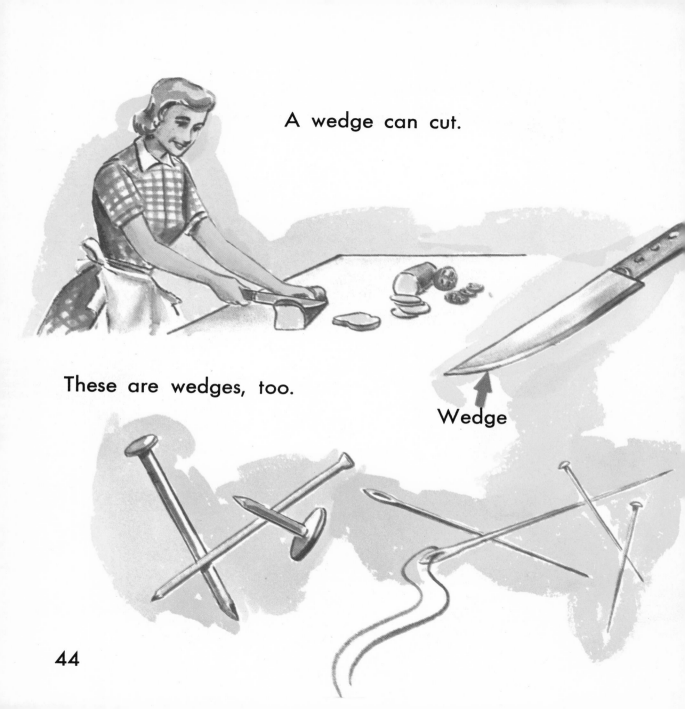

A wedge can cut.

These are wedges, too.

Wedge

BIG MACHINES

All of these machines have
simple machines in them.

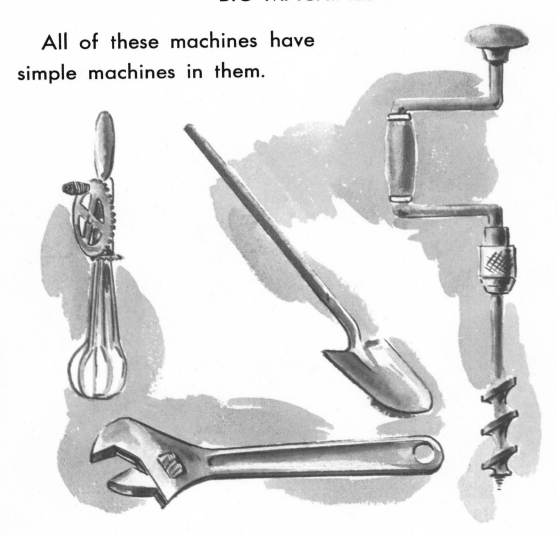

These have simple machines in them, too.

A machine as big as this is made
of many, many simple machines.

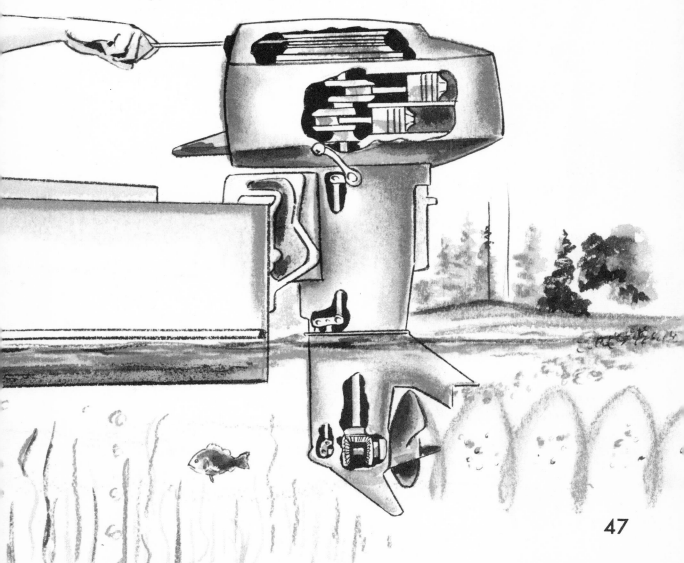

Vocabulary

The total vocabulary of this book is 120 words, excluding labels. Of these, 30 words (listed below in roman type) are first-grade level; 23 words (listed below in italic type) are above first-grade level. The words are listed in alphabetical order, and the numbers indicate the pages on which the words first appear.

across 8
airplane 35
along 29
animals 9

bicycles 23
block 32
board 34
boat 30
bringing 35

cannot 11
cars 22
cut 44

does 32
doing 13

elephant 30

far 18
flag 27

gears 20
goes 27

happens 18
hold 39

inclined 9

lever 6
log 13

machine 5
many 28
middle 15

more 33
move 8

numbers 32

off 30
other 21

people 5
plane 9
pull 17

pulley 8
putting 18

rock 12
roll 37
rope 26

screws 38
Simple 5
six 5

tackle 32
teeth 20
these 10
together 23
trains 36
turn 21

use 5

wagon 17
wedge 41
wheel 7

48